PUFFIN BOOKS

IS A CATERPILLAR TIC

This accessible collection of nearly two hundred poems covers a wide variety of different subjects and moods, including everything from magic to machines, pets to people and food to fairgrounds. There are poems by both classic and contemporary poets, taken from all around the world, and among the contributors are Margaret Mahy, Jack Prelutsky, Emily Dickinson, Elizabeth Jennings, A. A. Milne and many more familiar names. All the poems in the collection were chosen for their particular appeal to a young audience, and the warmth, colour, humour of the verse, combined with lively rhythms and vivid images, will capture every child's imagination.

Adrian Rumble is a headmaster, poet and also a successful anthologist. He is well known for his work with children and poetry.

C000077304

Is a Caterpillar Ticklish?

POEMS COLLECTED BY ADRIAN RUMBLE

Illustrated by Penny Dann

PUFFIN BOOKS

For Kristian, Joanna, Corinna and Dominic
with thanks to Shona McKellar

PUFFIN BOOKS

Published by the Penguin Group
27 Wrights Lane, London W8 5TZ, England
Viking Penguin Inc., 40 West 23rd Street, New York, New York 10010, USA
Penguin Books Australia Ltd, Ringwood, Victoria, Australia
Penguin Books Canada Ltd, 2801 John Street, Markham, Ontario, Canada L3R 1B4
Penguin Books (NZ) Ltd, 182–190 Wairau Road, Auckland 10, New Zealand

Penguin Books Ltd, Registered Offices: Harmondsworth, Middlesex, England

This anthology first published by Robert Royce Ltd 1986
Published in Puffin Books 1989
10 9 8 7 6 5 4 3

Made and printed in Great Britain by
Cox and Wyman Ltd, Reading, Berks.
Filmset in Linotron 202 Ehrhardt by
Rowland Phototypesetting Ltd, Bury St Edmunds, Suffolk

Contents

You may not believe it
Magic, the impossible and the slightly creepy

Halfway up the curving stair
Houses, building sites and streets

Rackerty, clackerty, clickerty, bong
Vehicles, machines and radios

Gingerbread pigs are better than pies

Food and drink

I blew a bubble from my pipe

Fairs and children at play

I've lots of pets, some small, some big

Pets

Secrets others never know

The beauty of everyday things, things observed differently

Cuckoo, cuckoo, what do you do?
Birds

Mostly me
Ourselves

I feel the summer in the spring
Weather and seasons

Skitter, scatter, leap and squeak

Animals

I knew a man who always wore a saucepan on his head

People

Get a move on, Joe, the stars are in the sky
Night

You may not believe it

Voices

Fly upon the summer shine
And sing upon the shade,
　Light wing and dark wing
　Called through the hollow glade.

O lean out of the window
Unwind your golden hair,
　The prince called to the princess
　Through the hollow air.

Follow me, O follow
Into the hollow hill,
　The witch called to the children:
　And the pale air was still.

Francis Scarfe

Chinese counting

Eenie, meenie, mackeracka,
Hi, di, dominacka,
Stickeracka, roomeracka,
Om, pom, push.

Anon

Higgledy, piggledy!

Higgledy, piggledy! See how they run!
Hopperty, popperty! What is the fun?
Has the sun or the moon tumbled into the sea?
What is the matter, now? Pray tell it me!

Higgledy, piggledy! How can I tell?
Hopperty, popperty! Hark to the bell!
The rats and the mice even scamper away;
Who can say what may not happen to-day?

Kate Greenaway

Indeed it is true

Indeed it is true, it is perfectly true;
    Believe me, indeed, I am playing no tricks;
An old man and his dog bide up there in the moon,
    And he's cross as a bundle of sticks.

Kate Greenaway

What's in there?

What's in there?
    Gold and money.
Where's my share?
    The mousie's run away with it.
Where's the mousie?
    In her housie.
Where's her housie?
    In the wood.
Where's the wood?
    The fire burnt it.
Where's the fire?
    The water quenched it.

Anon

The pumpkin

You may not believe it, for hardly could I:
I was cutting a pumpkin to put in a pie,
And on it was written in letters most plain
'You may hack me in slices, but I'll grow again.'

I seized it and sliced it and made no mistake
As, with dough rounded over, I put it to bake:
But soon in the garden as I chanced to walk,
Why there was that pumpkin entire on his stalk!

Robert Graves

My mother said

My mother said
    that I never should
Play with the gypsies
    in the wood.
The wood was dark,
The grass was green,
In came Sally
    with a tambourine.

Anon

The Twitchetty Witch

A Twitchetty Witch
Went hurtling by,
Twitchetty, Witchetty, Yooo-hooo-hooo!
Up in the dark
Where the black bats fly,
With her pointed nose
And her glittering eye,
A Twitchetty Witch
Went hurtling by,
Twitchetty, Witchetty-
S-w-w-i-i-i-s-shh!

Lillian Boucher

Halfway up the curving stair

The deserted house

There's no smoke in the chimney,
And the rain beats on the floor;
There's no glass in the window,
There's no wood in the door;
The heather grows behind the house,
And the sand lies before.

No hand hath trained the ivy,
The walls are grey and bare;
The boats upon the sea sail by,
Nor ever tarry there.
No beast of the field comes nigh,
Nor any bird of the air.

Mary Coleridge

House

The ruins of an old house stand
Without a roof, on muddy land,
Each window is a sightless eye
Staring at the city sky.

Locks are broken, every wall
Looks as if about to fall.
The people who lived here, they say,
Just packed up and went away.

And once when I was playing there
Halfway up the curving stair
I thought I heard a laughing sound
Coming from the trampled ground.

Leonard Clark

There's a red brick wall

There's a red brick wall
   along our street
that stands and burns
   in the sun's hot heat.

There aren't any flames
   but I know it burns.
When I walk by,
   it glows and turns
   my face to fire.

Nancy Chambers

The smoke

Over there
Is a little house
Quiet as a mouse,
Or an empty hive,
Or as death.
But up in the air
From the chimney-poke
Goes the gentle smoke,
And I know that the
    house is alive,
I can see its breath.

Eleanor Farjeon

Building site

Men in
   Miles of mud;
   A sloshing
   Wash.

Oceans of mud;
A rain
Drain.

Men like brown slugs on the
Drowned, brown, rain-washed plain.
   Straining cranes,
   Bucking trucks;
For men – too muddy much!

Pounds of caked mud
   Cling to each boot,
Mud-ball-and-chain
In that brown rain drain –
   How can they lift a foot?

But in the end
Houses do get built on the silt.

Marian Lines

Buildings

Buildings are a great surprise,
Every one's a different size.

Offices
grow
long
and
high,
tall
enough
to
touch
the
sky.

Houses seem
more like a box,
made of glue
and building blocks.

Every time you look, you see
Buildings shaped quite differently.

Myra Cohn Livingston

Rackerty, clackerty, clickerty, bong

Motor cars

From city window, 'way up high,
I like to watch the cars go by.
They look like burnished beetles, black,
That leave a little muddy track
Behind them as they slowly crawl.
Sometimes they do not move at all
But huddle close with hum and drone
As though they feared to be alone.
They grope their way through fog and night
With the golden feelers of their light.

Rowena Bastin Bennett

The radio men

When I was little more than six
I thought that men must be
Alive inside the radio
To act in plays, or simply blow
Trumpets, or sing to me.

I never got a glimpse of them,
They were so very small.
But I imagined them in there,
Their voices bursting on the air
Through that thin wooden wall.

Elizabeth Jennings

Car breakers

There's a graveyard in our street,
But it's not for putting people in;
The bodies that they bury here
Are made of steel and paint and tin.

The people come and leave their wrecks
For crunching in the giant jaws
Of a great hungry car-machine,
That lives on bonnets, wheels and doors.

When I pass by the yard at night,
I sometimes think I hear a sound
Of ghostly horns that moan and whine,
Upon that metal-graveyard mound.

Marian Lines

Funny the way different cars start

Funny the way
Different cars start.
Some with a chunk and a jerk,
Some with a cough and a puff of smoke
Out of the back,
Some with only a little click –
             with hardly any noise.

Funny the way
Different cars run.
Some rattle and bang,
Some whirrr,
Some knock and knock.
Some purr
And hummmmm
Smoothly on
             with hardly any noise.

Dorothy Baruch

The bulldozer

An orange-coated man
Who wears for his work
The colour of coat
You see in the dark
Starts the engine
Bang-b-bang-bang.

The bulldozer scoop
Is like a boot
As if a giant
Smoothed the ground
With the side of his foot
Down-d-down-down.

Digging its tracks
Into the mud
The yellow bulldozer
Bends its back
Like a butting bull
Charge-ch-charge-thud.

It lifts loose earth
Away from its feet
And drops it in a heap
Or dumps it into a truck
Bump-b-bump-full.

Stanley Cook

Engine No. 9

Engine, engine, number nine,
Sliding down Chicago line;
When she's polished she will shine,
Engine, engine, number nine.

Anon

Engineers

Pistons, valves and wheels and gears
That's the life of engineers.
Thumping, clunking engines going,
Hissing steam and whistles blowing.

There's not a place I'd rather be
Than working round machinery,
Listening to that clanking sound
Watching all the wheels go round.

Jimmy Garthwaite

Let's send a rocket

Ten, nine, eight . . .
Seven, six, five . . .

We'll send up a rocket,
And it will be LIVE.

Five, four, three . . .
It's ready to zoom!

We're counting each second,
And soon it will boom!

Get ready for . . . two;
Get ready to go . . .

It's TWO-and it's-ONE-
We're OFF! It's ZERO!

Kit Patrickson

Breakdown

Rackerty clackerty
clickerty BONG
the washing machine
has gone terribly wrong,

It's swallowed a button!
It's stuck in its jaw!
Do you think it will ever
get out any more?

Hark at it spluttering
clickerty-bump –
the washing is churning
all up in a lump,

And just for a button
so shiny and small!
O why did we ever
have buttons at all?

Rackerty clackerty
clickerty clack . . .
Hooray! THAT sounds better –
the button's come back!

Jean Kenward

Gingerbread pigs are better than pies

Drinking fountain

When I climb up
   To get a drink,
It doesn't work
   The way you'd think.

I turn it up.
   The water goes
And hits me right
   Upon the nose.

I turn it down
   To make it small
And don't get any
   Drink at all.

Marchette Chute

Water when you're thirsty

Drink it from a goblet,
Drink it from a cup.
Drink it when you're sitting down,
Or when you're standing up.
Drink it when you're very big,
Or very very small.
But drink it when you're thirsty,
And then it's best of all.

Clive Riche

The hardest thing to do
in the world

The hardest thing to do in the world
is stand in the hot sun
at the end of a long queue for ice creams
watching all the people who've just bought theirs
coming away from the queue
giving their ice creams their very first lick.

Michael Rosen

The peanut seller

Peanuts!
Two bags for five!

They brush your teeth,
They curl your hair;
They make you feel
Like a millionaire!

Peanuts!
Two bags for five!

Street cry from New Orleans

Shelling peas

I like to shell peas
that are fresh from a shop
I start at the tail end
instead of the top
so they will explode
with a wonderful pop!

Aileen Fisher

This is just to say

This is just to say
I have eaten
the plums
that were in
the icebox

and which
you were probably
saving
for breakfast

Forgive me
they were delicious
so sweet
and so cold

William Carlos Williams

Raw carrots

Raw carrots taste
Cool and hard,
Like some crisp metal.

Horses are
Fond of them,
Crunching up

The red gold
With much wet
Juice and noise.

Carrots must taste
To horses
As they do to us.

Valerie Worth

Sweet song

This is the sweet song,
Song of all the sweets,
Caramel and butterscotch
Bull's-eyes, raspberry treats;

Treacle toffee, acid drops,
Pastilles, crystal fruits,
Bubble-gum and liquorice-sticks
As black as new gum-boots;

Peppermint creams and aniseed balls,
Tiny sweets and whoppers,
Dolly-mixtures, chocolate drops,
Gigantic gob-stoppers;

Lemon sherbets, jelly babies,
Chocolate cream and flake,
Nougat, fudge and such as give
You tooth- and belly-ache.

Vernon Scannell

The Piccalilli Monster

Who's that coming
Walking down the street?
It's the Piccalilli Monster
With his big green feet.
It's the Piccalilli Monster
With his cauliflower nose
And his big yellow body
And his little green toes.

Oh the Piccalilli Monster
Is a very friendly chap
And he'll sit all day
With lots of children in his lap
And it doesn't really matter
If they get a little yellow
For the Piccalilli Monster
Is such a jolly fellow.

David Andrews

Gingerbread pigs

Ginger – ginger – gingerbread,
Make a pig and give him a head,
A curly tail and currants for eyes,
Gingerbread pigs are better than pies!

Safe indoors on a cold winter's night,
After the fires are set alight,
That's the time, so grandma said,
To eat little pigs made of gingerbread.

Daphne Lister

O me taters

O, me taters and me 'ot fried fish!
You can 'ave a little if you wish,
You can 'ave it on a plate or on a dish
    Or in a little bit o' paper!

Anon

Wake up, wake up, sleepy head

Wake up, wake up, sleepy head,
Look at mother baking bread;
A bowl, some flour,
Some salt,
And not least,
A grey, mysterious lump of yeast.

She mixes,
Presses,
Whips and stirs,
(Nobody's bread is as good as hers),
She pulls at it,
Folds it,
And pushes it small,
Draws it and fingers it into a ball;
Then into a bowl
Hid by a cloth,
And the yeast gets to work as quiet as a moth.

At the end of an hour the children cry,
OH,
At the cloth lifted high by a mountain of
Dough.
Push it and pull it
And knead it once more,
And put it in the oven
And close up the door.

And, oh, when they're baked
All crispy and brown
They're the best cottage loaves
You will find in the town.

Gregory Harrison

On tomato ketchup

If you do not shake the bottle,
None'll come, and then a lot'll.

Anon

I eat my peas with honey

I eat my peas with honey,
I've done it all my life:
It makes the peas taste funny,
But it keeps them on the knife.

Anon

I blew a bubble from my pipe

Fairground

Organ-shout music, kaleidoscope streamers,
Big-Dipper hooters and Dodge-'Em Car
   screamers,
Roundabout motors and buses and steamers,
'Walk up, folks . . .
'Walk up, folks, come to the . . .'

Ear-splitting shooting range, trot-trotting donkeys,
Blue and red cockatoos, clambering monkeys,
Crowd noises, loud noises, shrill honky-tonkies.
'Walk up, folks . . .
'Walk up, folks, come to the . . .'

Gypsy magicians, and goldfish for prizes,
Candy-floss sugar in gigantic sizes,
Heart-stopping Ghost Train with screeching
   surprises,
'Walk up, folks . . .
'Walk up, folks, come to the Fair. Come to the
   Fair!'

Marian Lines

The merry-go-round

The merry-go-round
   whirls round and round
   in a giant circle on the ground.
And the horses run
   an exciting race
   while the wind blows music in your face.
Then the whole world spins
   to a coloured tune
   but the ride is over much too soon.

Myra Cohn Livingston

Mine

I made a sand castle.
In rolled the sea.
    'All sand castles
    belong to me –
    to me,'
said the sea.

I dug sand tunnels.
In flowed the sea.
    'All sand tunnels
    belong to me –
    to me,'
said the sea.

I saw my sand pail floating free.
I ran and snatched it from the sea.
    'My sand pail
    belongs to me –
    to ME!'

Lilian Moore

Will you be my little wife?

Will you be my little wife,
  If I ask you? Do!
I'll buy you such a Sunday frock,
  A nice umbrella, too.

And you shall have a little hat,
  With such a long white feather,
A pair of gloves, and sandal shoes,
  The softest kind of leather.

And you shall have a tiny house,
  A beehive full of bees,
A little cow, a largish cat,
  And green sage cheese.

Kate Greenaway

A swing song

    Swing, swing,
    Sing, sing,
Here! my throne
and I am king!
    Swing, sing,
    Swing, sing,
Farewell, earth,
for I'm on the wing!

Low, high,
Here I fly,
Like a bird
through sunny sky;
Free, free,
Over the lea,
Over the mountain,
over the sea!

Up, down,
Up, down,
Which is the way
to London town?
Where? Where?
Up in the air,
Close your eyes and
now you are there!
No, no,
Low, low,
Sweeping daisies
with my toe.
Slow, slow,
To and fro,
Slow – slow – slow – slow.

William Allingham

Seven fat fishermen

Seven fat fishermen,
Sitting side by side,
Fished from a bridge,
By the banks of the Clyde.

The first caught a tiddler,
The second caught a crab,
The third caught a winkle,
The fourth caught a dab.

The fifth caught a tadpole,
The sixth caught an eel,
But the seventh, he caught
An old cartwheel.

Anon

A skip to beat bad temper

An angry tiger in a cage
Will roar and roar with rage,
And gnash his teeth and lash his tail,
For that's how tigers rant and rail.
I keep my temper in a cage,
I hate it when it roars with rage,
I hate its teeth, I hate its tail,
So when it starts to rant and rail,
I tell my mum, I tell my dad,
I tell them why it's feeling bad,
And then I skip and skip and skip,
And lash my rope just like a whip
And when I skip because I'm cross,
My temper-tiger knows who's boss,
And when I've skipped and whipped like mad,
My temper-tiger's not so bad.
I have to keep it tame this way,
Or it will eat me up one day.

Cynthia Mitchell

Waiting

Waiting, waiting, waiting
  For the party to begin;
Waiting, waiting, waiting
  For the laughter and din;
Waiting, waiting, waiting
  With hair just so
And clothes trim and tidy
  From top-knot to toe.
The floor is all shiny,
  The lights are ablaze;
There are sweetmeats in plenty
  And cakes beyond praise.
Oh the games and dancing,
  The tricks and the toys
The music and the madness,
  The colour and noise!
Waiting, waiting, waiting
  For the first knock on the door –
Was ever such waiting,
  Such waiting before?

James Reeves

Adventure

It's not very far to the edge of town
Where trees look up and hills look down,
We go there almost every day
To climb and swing and paddle and play.

It's not very far to the edge of town,
Just up one little hill and down,
And through one gate, and over two stiles –
But coming home it's miles and miles.

Harry Behn

Soap bubbles

Fill the pipe and gently blow,
Watch the bubbles slowly grow.
Toss them lightly in the air,
Floating softly off they go.

High and higher in the sky,
Rainbow coloured, bright and gay,
Every moment growing smaller,
Till they melt and vanish away.

Maisie Cobby

The broken toys

In the broken box
The broken toys –
   Dusty,
Battered and rusty,
Tattered and torn,
   Forlorn, forlorn.

The snapped strings
And the busted springs,
The rag-doll raggy and rent,
The pink tin tea-set buckled and bent,
   The crashed plane,
   The car, the train –
Smashed in a terrible accident.

And all the dolls' eyes
Rolling loose like heavy marbles
Up the doll's house stairs and down
The stairs of the overturned house . . .
The dead wheels of a clockwork mouse.

In the broken box
The broken toys –
   Dusty,
Battered and rusty,
Tattered and torn,
   Forlorn, forlorn.

James Kirkup

Thumping, stumping, bumping, jumping

Thumping, stumping, bumping, jumping,
Ripping, nipping, tripping, skipping,
All the way home.

Popping, clopping, stopping, hopping,
Stalking, chalking, talking, walking,
All the way home.

Anon

Bubble

I blew a bubble from my pipe
It drifted on and on –
I blew another one and thought –
'Where has the first one gone?'

Jacqueline Segal

I've lots of pets,
some small, some big

A small dragon

I've found a small dragon in the woodshed.
Think it must have come from deep inside a forest
because it's damp and green and leaves
are still reflecting in its eyes.

I fed it on many things, tried grass,
the roots of stars, hazel-nut and dandelion,
but it stared up at me as if to say, I need
foods you can't provide.

It made a nest among the coal,
not unlike a bird's but larger,
it is out of place here
and is quite silent.

If you believed in it I would come
hurrying to your house to let you share my wonder,
but I want instead to see
if you yourself will pass this way.

Brian Patten

Grandpa Tortoise

Grandpa Tortoise –
He's so slow . . .
Do you think
he'll EVER go?
Grandpa Tortoise
can't decide
whether it
is nice outside,
or, if it
is nicer IN.
He just thinks
he may begin
moving . . . moving
carefully
over to
the apple tree . . .

When he's thought
a little . . . when
he has thought
that thought again . . .
maybe he
will move a bit –
(when he's sort of
            thought of
                    it).

Jean Kenward

The rescue

The wind is loud,
The wind is blowing,
The waves are big,
The waves are growing.
What's that? What's that?
A dog is crying,
It's in the sea,
A dog is crying.
His or hers
Or yours or mine?
A dog is crying,
A dog is crying.

Is no one there?
A boat is going,
The waves are big,
A man is rowing,
The waves are big,
The waves are growing.
Where's the dog?
It isn't crying.
His or hers
Or yours or mine?
Is it dying?
Is it dying?

The wind is loud,
The wind is blowing,
The waves are big,
The waves are growing.
Where's the boat?
It's upside down.
And where's the dog,
And must it drown?
His or hers
Or yours or mine?
O, must it drown?
O, must it drown?

Where's the man?
He's on the sand,
So tired and wet
He cannot stand.
And where's the dog?
It's in his hand,
He lays it down
Upon the sand.
His or hers
Or yours or mine?
The dog is mine,
The dog is mine!

So tired and wet
And still it lies.
I stroke its head,
It opens its eyes,
It wags its tail,
So tired and wet.

I call its name,
For it's my pet,
Not his or hers
Or yours, but mine –
And up it gets,
And up it gets!

Ian Serraillier

Market square

I had a penny,
A bright new penny,
I took my penny
    To the market square.
I wanted a rabbit,
A little brown rabbit,
And I looked for a rabbit
    'Most everywhere.

For I went to the stall where they sold sweet
    lavender
('Only a penny for a bunch of lavender!')
'Have you got a rabbit, 'cos I don't want lavender?'
    But they hadn't got a rabbit, not anywhere there.

I had a penny,
And I had another penny,
I took my pennies
    To the market square.
I did want a rabbit,
A little baby rabbit,
And I looked for rabbits
    'Most everywhere.

And I went to the stall where they sold fresh
        mackerel
('Now then! Tuppence for a fresh-caught
        mackerel!')
'Have you got a rabbit, 'cos I don't like mackerel?'
    But they hadn't got a rabbit, not anywhere there.

I found a sixpence,
A little white sixpence.
I took it in my hand
    To the market square.
I was buying my rabbit
(I do like rabbits),
And I looked for my rabbit
    'Most everywhere.

So I went to the stall where they sold fine
        saucepans
('Walk up, walk up, sixpence for a saucepan!')
'Could I have a rabbit, 'cos we've got two
        saucepans?'
    But they hadn't got a rabbit, not anywhere there.

I had nuffin',
No, I hadn't got nuffin',
So I didn't go down
    To the market square;
But I walked on the common
The old-gold common . . .
And I saw little rabbits
    'Most everywhere!

So I'm sorry for the people who sell fine
        saucepans,
I'm sorry for the people who sell fresh mackerel,
I'm sorry for the people who sell sweet lavender,
    'Cos they haven't got a rabbit, not anywhere
        there!

A. A. Milne

Good morning, cat

Good morning, cat,
    you're in my yard
    and sniffing for a mouse;
    you might as well give up – because
    he's hiding in the house.

Myra Cohn Livingston

Our cat

Our cat likes apple crumble,
With or without cream,
She eats it though I've told her
That it will make her dream,
And sometimes she eats custard,
Though it's sure to make her fat,
Then she purrs and licks her whiskers
And thinks, 'What a lucky cat!'

Daphne Lister

Cat purring

Cat
purring

four furry paws
walking

delicate-
ly

      between
flower stems
stalking

butter-
flies.

Keith Bosley

Cat!

     Cat!
     Scat!
Atter her, atter her,
Sleeky flatterer,
Spitfire chatterer,
Scatter her, scatter her
     Off her mat!
     Wuff!
     Wuff!
     Treat her rough!
Git her, git her,
Whiskery spitter!
Catch her, catch her,
Green-eyed scratcher!
     Slathery
     Slithery
     Hisser,
     Don't, miss her!
Run till you're dithery,
     Hithery
     Thithery
     Pfitts! pfitts!
     How she spits!
     Spitch! Spatch!
     Can't she scratch!
Scratching the bark
Of the sycamore-tree,
She's reached her ark
And's hissing at me

Pfitts! pfitts!
Wuff! wuff!
Scat,
Cat!
That's
That!

Eleanor Farjeon

The cat

Within that porch, across the way,
    I see two naked eyes this night;
Two eyes that neither shut nor blink,
    Searching my face with a green light.

But cats to me are strange, so strange –
    I cannot sleep if one is near;
And though I'm sure I see those eyes,
    I'm not so sure a body's there!

W. H. Davies

Where are you going?

Where are you going,
My little cat?

I am going to town,
To get me a hat.

What! A hat for a cat!
A cat get a hat!
Who ever saw a cat with a hat?

Anon

Under the willow

Under the willow
With a leaf stuck in his mouth
The puppy sleeps

Issa

Dogs

I had a little dog,
   and my dog was very small.
He licked me in the face,
   and he answered to my call.
Of all the treasures that were mine,
   I loved him best of all.

Frances Cornford

Puppy and I

I met a man as I went walking;
We got talking,
Man and I.
'Where are you going to, Man?' I said
   (I said to the Man as he went by).
'Down to the village, to get some bread.
   Will you come with me?' 'No, not I.'

I met a horse as I went walking;
We got talking,
Horse and I.
'Where are you going to, Horse, today?'
   (I said to the horse as he went by).
'Down to the village to get some hay.
   Will you come with me?' 'No, not I.'

I met a Woman as I went walking;
We got talking,
Woman and I.
'Where are you going to, Woman, so early?'
  (I said to the Woman as she went by).
'Down to the village to get some barley.
  Will you come with me?' 'No, not I.'

I met some Rabbits as I went walking;
We got talking,
Rabbits and I.
'Where are you going in your brown fur coats?'
  (I said to the Rabbits as they went by).
'Down to the village to get some oats.
  Will you come with us?' 'No, not I.'

I met a puppy as I went walking;
We got talking,
Puppy and I.
'Where are you going to this nice fine day?'
  (I said to the puppy as he went by).
'Up in the hills to roll and play.'
  '*I'll* come with you, Puppy,' said I.

A. A. Milne

Me and my dog

Me and my dog
have tramped together
in cold weather
and hot.

Me and my dog
don't care whether
we get any work
or not.

Anon

The little turtle

There was a little turtle.
He lived in a box.
He swam in a puddle.
He climbed on the rocks.

He snapped at a mosquito.
He snapped at a flea.
He snapped at a minnow.
And he snapped at me.

He caught the mosquito.
He caught the flea.
He caught the minnow.
But he didn't catch me.

Vachel Lindsay

Secrets others never know

Yellow weed

How did you get here,
weed?
Who brought your seed?

Did it lift
on the wind and
sail
and drift
from a far and yellow
field?

Was your seed a
burr,
a sticky burr that
clung to a
fox's
furry tail?

Did it fly with a
bird
who liked to feed
on the tasty
seed
of the yellow
weed?
How did you come?

Lilian Moore

Song of the seashore

The soft waves lisp,
On the stone-spangled shore,
Shining and shimmering,
Murmuring 'More . . .
More music, please . . .'
And the stones sigh and ride
And whisper their songs
To the incoming tide.

Daphne Lister

Noise

Billy is blowing his trumpet;
Bertie is banging a tin;
Betty is crying for mummy
And Bob has pricked Ben with a pin.
Baby is crying out loudly;
He's out on the lawn in his pram.
I am the only one silent
And I've eaten all of the jam.

Anon

Grim and gloomy

Oh, grim and gloomy,
So grim and gloomy
Are the caves beneath the sea.
Oh, rare but roomy
And bare and boomy,
Those salt sea caverns be.

Oh, slim and slimy
Or grey and grimy
Are the animals of the sea.
Salt and oozy
And safe and snoozy
The caves where those animals be.

Hark to the shuffling,
Huge and snuffling,
Ravenous, cavernous, great sea-beasts!
But fair and fabulous,
Tintinnabulous,
Gay and fabulous are their feasts.

Ah, but the queen of the sea,
The querulous, perilous sea!
How the curls of her tresses
The pearls on her dresses,
Sway and swirl in the waves,
How cosy and dozy,
How sweet ring-a-rosy
Her bower in the deep-sea caves!

Oh, rare but roomy
And bare and boomy
Those caverns under the sea,
And grave and grandiose,
Safe and sandiose
The dens of her denizens be.

James Reeves

Which is the way to Somewhere Town?

Which is the way to Somewhere Town?
　　Oh, up in the morning early;
Over the tiles and the chimney-pots,
　　That is the way, quite clearly.

And which is the door to Somewhere Town?
　　Oh, up in the morning early;
The round red sun is the door to go through,
　　That is the way, quite clearly.

Kate Greenaway

Sea shore

Sandy shore and sea-weed;
Rocks and cockle-shells;
Pebbles round and salty;
Dead fish smells.

Sun on bending water;
Donkeys jingling bells;
Hoofprints in sand-ripples;
Salt-water wells.

Boats against the sunshine;
Seagulls' squealing hells;
Spray on brown faces;
Small boys' yells.

John Kitching

The hat

Somebody gave me a hat.
It has three feathers and it's sort of flat.
I tried it on my brother.
I tried it on the cat.
And then I tried it on myself.
It looked too fat.
You may have it.
If you'd like it.
It's a sort of fat flat hat.

Karla Kuskin

Sunrise

I've never seen the great sun rise,
For then I am in bed;
The sands of slumber in my eyes
Hold down my drowsy head.

I think the sun climbs up the sky
And throws the clouds away,
Then girds her flaming tunic high
And strides to meet the day.

Soft-touched by birds' wings is her head,
Her feet caressed by trees;
She turns their leaves to gold and red
And stoops to drink the seas.

Katherine Kosmak

What is white?

White is a dove
And lily of the valley
And a puddle of milk
Spilled in an alley –
A ship's sail
A kite's tail
A wedding veil

Hailstones and
Halibut bones
And some people's
Telephones.
The hottest and most blinding light
Is white.
And breath is white.
When you blow it out on a frosty night.
White is the shining absence of all colour
Then absence is white
Out of touch
Out of sight.
White is marshmallow
And vanilla ice-cream
And the part you can't remember
In a dream.
White is the sound
Of a light foot walking
White is a pair of
Whispers talking.
White is the beautiful
Broken lace
Of snowflakes falling
On your face.
You can smell white
In a country room
Near the end of May
When the cherries bloom.

Mary O'Neil

Morning

Will there really be a morning?
   Is there such a thing as day?
Could I see it from the mountains
   If I were as tall as they?
Has it feet like water lilies?
   Has it feathers like a bird?
Is it brought from famous countries
   Of which I've never heard?
Oh, some scholar! Oh, some sailor!
   Oh, some wise man from the skies!
Please to tell a little pilgrim,
   Where the place called morning lies!

Emily Dickinson

What is black?

Black is the night
When there isn't a star
And you can't tell by looking
Where you are.
Black is a pail of paving tar.
Black is jet
And things you'd like to forget.
Black is a chimney
Black is a cat,
A leopard, a raven,
A silk top hat.

The sound of black is
'Boom! Boom! Boom!'
Echoing in
An empty room.
Black is kind –
It covers up
The shabby street,
The broken cup.
Black is the coal
That drives a train
The soot spots on
The window pane.
Black is a feeling
Hard to explain
Like suffering but
Without the pain.
Black is liquorice
And patent leather shoes,
Black is the print
In the news.
Black is beauty
In its deepest form,
The darkest cloud
In a thunderstorm.
Think of what starlight
And lamplight would lack
Diamonds and fireflies
If they couldn't lean against
Black . . .

Mary O'Neil

Otherwise

There must be magic,
Otherwise,
How could day turn to night,

And how could sailboats,
Otherwise,
Go sailing out of sight,

And how could peanuts,
Otherwise,
Be covered up so tight?

Aileen Fisher

Whispers

Whispers
    tickle through your ear
    telling things you like to hear.

Whispers
    are as soft as skin
    letting little words curl in.

Whispers
    come so they can blow
    secrets others never know.

Myra Cohn Livingston

Roads go ever ever on

Roads go ever ever on,
    Over rock and under tree,
By caves where never sun has shone,
    By streams that never find the sea;
Over snow by winter sown,
    And through the merry flowers of June,
Over grass and over stone,
    And under mountains in the moon.

J. R. R. Tolkien

Scarecrow independence

I may look raggy and queer
– but I bow to no man.

My face may look silly and sad
– but I'm no snowman.

I may stand stiff and still
– but hold my head high.

I raise my old top hat to no one
– not even when YOU walk by.

James Kirkup

Mud

I like mud.
    I like it on my clothes.
I like it on my fingers.
    I like it in my toes.

Dirt's pretty ordinary
    And dust's a dud.
For a really good mess-up
    I like mud.

John Smith

The jumble sale

Scrimble, scramble, scrumble,
Search around amongst the jumble,
I love the rough-and-tumble
Of a jumble sale.

There are jam-jars, jeans and jackets,
Old toys and tennis racquets
And home-made sweets in packets
At the jumble sale.

There's a big old-fashioned mangle,
A pair of ear-rings that dangle
And some coloured bells that jangle
At the jumble sale.

There are pots and pans and dishes
And round glass bowls for fishes
Whatever you might wish is
At the jumble sale.

There are picture frames, so dusty,
Old books that smell all musty
And a sword that's slightly rusty
At the jumble sale.

People crowd and crush together
No matter what the weather –
You might find an ostrich feather
At the jumble sale.

So scrimble, scramble, scrumble,
Search around amongst the jumble,
Enjoy the rough-and-tumble
Of the jumble sale.

Daphne Lister

Brooms

On stormy days
When the wind is high
Tall trees are brooms
Sweeping the sky.

They swish their branches
In buckets of rain,
And swash and sweep it
Blue again.

Dorothy Aldis

Trees

Trees are the kindest things I know,
They do no harm, they simply grow

And spread a shade for sleepy cows,
And gather birds among their boughs.

They give us fruit in leaves above,
And wood to make our houses of,

And leaves to burn on Hallowe'en,
And in the Spring new buds of green.

They are the first when day's begun
To touch the beams of morning sun,

They are the last to hold the light
When evening changes into night,

And when a moon floats on the sky
They hum a drowsy lullaby
Of sleepy children long ago . . .
Trees are the kindest things I know.

Harry Behn

Cuckoo, cuckoo, what do you do?

The Mirror

Between the woods the afternoon
Is fallen in a golden swoon.
The sun looks down from quiet skies
To where a quiet water lies,
  And silent trees stoop down to trees.
And there I saw a white swan make
Another white swan in the lake;
And, breast to breast, both motionless,
They waited for the wind's caress . . .
  And all the water was at ease.

A. A. Milne

Dawn

The thrush is tapping a stone
With a snail's shell in its beak;
A small bird hangs from a cherry
Until the stem shall break.
No waking song has begun,
And yet birds chatter and hurry
And throng in the elm's gloom,
Because an owl goes home.

Gordon Bottomly

Seven blackbirds in a tree

Seven blackbirds in a tree,
Count them and see what they be.
One for sorrow
Two for joy
Three for a girl
Four for a boy;
Five for silver
Six for gold
Seven for a secret
That's never been told.

Anon

Little bird

Little hurt bird
in my hand
your heart beats
like the pound of the sea
under the warmth
of your soft feathers.

Charlotte Zolotow

Three little girls

Three little girls were sitting on a rail,
            Sitting on a rail,
            Sitting on a rail;
Three little girls were sitting on a rail,
On a fine hot day in September.

What did they talk about that fine day,
            That fine day,
            That fine day?
What did they talk about that fine day,
That fine hot day in September?

The crows and the corn they talked about,
            Talked about,
            Talked about;
But nobody knows what was said by the crows,
On that fine hot day in September.

Kate Greenaway

Chick, chick, chatterman

Chick, chick, chatterman
  How much are your geese?
Chick, chick, chatterman
  Five cents apiece.
Chick, chick, chatterman
  That's too dear.
Chick, chick, chatterman
  Get out of here.

Anon (Traditional American)

Bird sips water

Bird
sips water
drips music
throwing back its head

Throw back your head
turn the rain
into a song
and you will fly

Keith Bosley

Cuckoo

Cuckoo, Cuckoo,
What do you do?

In April
I open my bill.

In May
I sing night and day.

In June
I change my tune.

In July
Up high I fly.

In August
Away I must.

Anon

Toucans two

Whatever one toucan can do
is sooner done by toucans two,
and three toucans (it's very true)
can do much more than two can do.

And toucans numbering two plus two can
manage more than all the zoo can.
In short, there is no toucan who can
do what four or three or two can.

Jack Prelutsky

Wild black crows

Oh the wild black crows
The wild black crows
Fly far away to where nobody knows,
Where nobody knows and nobody goes,
Nobody knows
But the wild black crows.

Margaret Wise Brown

Two little blackbirds

Two little blackbirds singing in the sun,
One flew away and then there was one.
One little blackbird, very black and small,
He flew away and then there was the wall.
One little brick wall lonely in the rain,
Waiting for the blackbirds to come and sing again.

Anon

Sea gull

The sea gull curves his wings,
   the sea gull turns his eyes.
Get down into the water, fish!
         (if you are wise.)

The sea gull slants his wings,
   the sea gull turns his head.
Get deep into the water, fish!
         (or you'll be dead.)

Elizabeth Coatsworth

The old grey goose

Go and tell Aunt Nancy,
Go and tell Aunt Nancy,
Go and tell Aunt Nancy,
   The old grey goose is dead.

The one that she was saving,
The one that she was saving,
The one that she was saving,
   To make a feather bed.

She died on Friday,
She died on Friday,
She died on Friday,
   Behind the old barn shed.

She left nine little goslings,
She left nine little goslings,
She left nine little goslings,
   To scratch for their own bread.

Anon

Little Robin Redbreast

Little Robin Redbreast sat upon a tree,
Up went Pussy-cat, and down went he.
Down came Pussy-cat, and away Robin ran;
Says little Robin Redbreast, 'Catch me if you can!'

Little Robin Redbreast flew upon a wall,
Pussy-cat jumped after him, and almost had a fall.
Little Robin chirped and sang; and what did Pussy
   say?
Pussy-cat said 'Mew', and Robin flew away.

Anon

Mostly me

Hands

Hands
handling
dangling in water
making and shaking
slapping and clapping
warming and warning
hitting and fitting
grabbing and rubbing
peeling and feeling
taking and breaking
helping and giving
lifting
sifting sand
hand holding
hand.

Peter Young

Reflection

In the mirror
I can see
Lots of things
But mostly – me.

Myra Cohn Livingston

Hair

I despair
About hair
   With all the fuss
   For us
Of snipping
And clipping,
   Of curling
   And twirling,
Of tying
And drying,
   And lopping
   And flopping,
And flurries
And worries,
   About strength
   The length,
As it nears
The ears
   Or shoulder.
   When you're older
It turns grey
Or goes away
   Or leaves a fuzz
   Hair does!

Max Fatchen

It was long ago

I'll tell you, shall I, something I remember?
Something that still means a great deal to me.
It was long ago.

A dusty road in summer I remember,
A mountain, and an old house, and a tree
That stood, you know,

Behind the house. An old woman I remember
In a red shawl with a grey cat on her knee
Humming under a tree.

She seemed the oldest thing I can remember,
But then perhaps I was not more than three.
It was long ago.

I dragged on the dusty road, and I remember
How the old woman looked over the fence at me
And seemed to know

How it felt to be three, and called out, I remember
'Do you like bilberries and cream for tea?'
I went under the tree

And while she hummed, and the cat purred, I
    remember
How she filled a saucer with berries and cream for
    me
So long ago,

Such berries and such cream as I remember
I never had seen before and never see
Today, you know.

And that is almost all I can remember,
The house, the mountain, the grey cat on her knee,
Her red shawl, and the tree,

And the taste of the berries, the feel of the sun
            I remember,
And the smell of everything that used to be
So long ago,

Till the heat on the road outside again I remember,
And how the long dusty road seemed to have for
  me
No end, you know.

That is the farthest thing I can remember.
It won't mean much to you. It does to me.
Then I grew up, you see.

Eleanor Farjeon

I speak, I say, I talk

Cats purr.
Lions roar.
Owls hoot.
Bears snore.
Crickets creak.
Mice squeak.
Sheep baa.
But I SPEAK!

Monkeys chatter.
Cows moo.
Ducks quack.
Doves coo.
Pigs squeal.
Horses neigh.
Chickens cluck.
But I SAY!

Flies hum.
Dogs growl.
Bats screech.
Coyotes howl.
Frogs croak.
Parrots squawk.
Bees buzz.
But I TALK!

Arnold L. Shapiro

Sneezing

Sneeze on Monday, sneeze for danger;
Sneeze on Tuesday, meet a stranger;
Sneeze on Wednesday, sneeze for a letter;
Sneeze on Thursday, something better;
Sneeze on Friday, sneeze for sorrow –
Sneeze on Saturday, see your sweetheart
    tomorrow.

Traditional

The features

Eye winker,
Tom Tinker,
Nose smeller,
Mouth eater,
Chin chopper,
Guzzlewhopper.

Anon

Old John Braddle-um

Number One, Number One,
Now my song has just begun,
   With a rum-tum-taddle-um,
   Old John Braddle-um,
   Eh! what country folks we be.

Number Two, Number Two,
Some likes a boot but I likes a shoe,
   With a . . .

Number Three, Number Three,
Some likes coffee, but I likes tea,
   With a . . .

Number Four, Number Four,
Some likes a gate but I likes a door
   With a . . .

Number Five, Number Five,
Some likes 'em dead but I likes 'em alive,
   With a . . .

Number Six, Number Six,
Some likes stones but I likes sticks,
   With a . . .

Number Seven, Number Seven,
Is just the same as Number Eleven,
   With a . . .

Number Eight, Number Eight,
Some likes a door but I likes a gate,
  With a . . .

Number Nine, Number Nine,
Some likes ale but I likes wine,
  With a . . .

Number Ten, Number Ten,
Some likes a cock but I likes a hen,
  With a . . .

Number Eleven, Number Eleven,
Is just the same as Number Seven,
  With a . . .

Number Twelve, Number Twelve,
If you want any more you can say it yourself,
  With a . . .

Anon

This is the hand

This is the hand
that touched the frost
that froze my tongue
and made it numb

This is the hand
that cracked the nut
that went in my mouth
and never came out

This is the hand
that slid round the bath
to find the soap
that wouldn't float

This is the hand
on the hot water bottle
meant to warm my bed
that got lost instead

This is the hand
that held the bottle
that let go of the soap
that cracked the nut
that touched the frost
this is the hand
that never gets lost.

Michael Rosen

Jump or jiggle

Frogs jump
Caterpillars hump

Worms wiggle
Bugs jiggle

Rabbits hop
Horses clop

Snakes slide
Sea gulls glide

Mice creep
Deer leap

Puppies bounce
Kittens pounce

Lions stalk –
But –
I walk!

Evelyn Beyer

Intelligence test

'What do you use your eyes for?'
The white-coated man inquired.
'I use my eyes for looking,'
Said Toby, ' – unless I'm tired.'

'I see. And then you close them,'
Observed the white-coated man.
'Well done. A very good answer.
Let's try another one.

'What is your nose designed for?
What use is the thing to you?'
'I use my nose for smelling,'
Said Toby, 'Don't you, too?'

'I do indeed,' said the expert,
'That's what the thing is for.
Now I've another question to ask you,
Then there won't be any more.

'What are your ears intended for?
Those things at each side of your head?
Come on – don't be shy – I'm sure you can say.'
'For washing behind,' Toby said.

Vernon Scannell

I feel the summer in the spring

The dragon

I saw a cloud like a dragon,
Lying in wait in the sky,
With a purple head and a purple tail
And a little blue patch for an eye.

From his snout came flames of fire,
And he began to run,
Chasing the daylight away to the west
And fighting the setting sun!

Daphne Lister

Thunder

I hear
the drummers
strike
the sky.

Glenys Van Every

Rain

Beautiful rain
Falling so softly
Such a delicate thing

The harvests need you
And some of the flowers
But we too

Because you remind
Of coolness of quiet
Of tenderest words

Come down rain, fall
Not too harshly but give
Your strange sense of peace to us.

Elizabeth Jennings

The rain fell

The rain fell –
    the rain fell –
the rain in our
    gutter –
it came with
    a great sigh,

it came with
   a splutter
of garbage
   and loose leaves
and matchsticks
   and berries
and cartons
   and corktops
and stones of old
   cherries.

I took off –
   I took off
my shoes,
   and I paddled:
I waded
   in rivers,
and wandered
   and waddled
along by
   the drain where
the water fell –
   dashing
with bubbles
   and turmoil
and sploshing
   and splashing.

The rain went –
   the rain went –
The great sky
   shone splendid,

as if it were
　suddenly
patched up
　and mended.
The lane glinted
　bright as
a new-minted
　penny.
And rain?
　You might guess
that there's never
　been any!

Jean Kenward

April rain song

Let the rain kiss you.
Let the rain beat upon your head with silver liquid
　drops.
Let the rain sing you a lullaby.

The rain makes still pools on the sidewalk.
The rain makes running pools in the gutter.
The rain plays a little sleep-song on our roof at
　night –

And I love the rain.

Langston Hughes

Spring

As my eyes
search
the prairie
I feel the summer
in the spring.

Chippewa Indian poem
(Translated by F. Densmore)

Barefoot days

In the morning, very early,
That's the time I love to go
Barefoot where the fern grows curly
And grass is cool between each toe,
On a summer morning – O!
On a summer morning!

That is when the birds go by
Up the sunny slopes of air,
And each rose has a butterfly
Or a golden bee to wear;
And I am glad in every toe –
Such a summer morning – O!
Such a summer morning!

Rachel Field

October

The summer is over,
   The trees are all bare,
There is mist in the garden
   And frost in the air.
The meadows are empty
   And gathered the sheaves –
But isn't it lovely
   Kicking up leaves!

John from the garden
   Has taken the chairs;
It's dark in the evening
   And cold on the stairs.
Winter is coming
   And everyone grieves –
But isn't it lovely
   Kicking up leaves!

Rose Fyleman

April

The roofs are shining from the rain,
   The sparrows twitter as they fly,
And with a windy April grace
   The little clouds go by.

Yet the back yards are bare and brown
   With only one unchanging tree –
I could not be so sure of Spring
   Save that it sings to me.

Sara Teasdale

Autumn song

These are the days of falling leaves,
   The days of hazy weather,
Smelling of gold chrysanthemums
   And grey wood smoke together.

These are the nights of nearby stars,
   The nights of closer moons,
When the windy darkness echoes
   To crickets' farewell tunes.

Elizabeth-Ellen Long

November

November comes,
And November goes
With the last red berries
And the first white snows,

With night coming early
And dawn coming late,
And ice in the bucket
And frost by the gate.

The fires burn
And the kettles sing,
And earth sinks to rest
Until next spring.

Elizabeth Coatsworth

Cynthia in the snow

It sushes.
It hushes
The loudness in the road.
It flitters-twitters,
And laughs away from me.
It laughs a lovely whiteness,
And whitely whirs away,
To be
Some otherwhere,
Still white as milk or shirts.
So beautiful it hurts.

Gwendolyn Brooks

Ice

When it is the winter time
    I run up the street
And make the ice laugh
    With my little feet –
'Crickle, crackle, crickle
    Crrreeet, crrreeet, crrreeet.'

Dorothy Aldis

Snowy morning

Wake
gently this morning
to a different day.
Listen.

There is no bray
of buses,
no brake growls,
no siren howls and
no horns
blow.
There is only
the silence
of a city
hushed
by snow.

Lilian Moore

Hinkum, dankum

Hinkum, dankum,
what do you say?
Somebody came here
yesterday –

Somebody delicate
small and light
paid a visit here
yesternight.

Quietly, quietly,
heel and toe,
nobody saw him
come or go,

Icicles quivering
on his shoe,
frost at forehead
and finger too:

Sleek and sinuous
frail and fair
never a movement
heard we there.

Hinkum, dankum,
what do you know?
Somebody left us
Sleeping . . .
                    snow.

Jean Kenward

Snow clouds

Like sulky polar bears
Clouds prowl across the winter sky
From cold and snowy northern lands
As though from icy lairs.

Soon snow begins to fall
Small snippets of the whitest fur
And like the stealthy polar bear
It makes no sound at all.

Daphne Lister

Little wind

Little wind, blow on the hill-top,
Little wind, blow down the plain;
Little wind, blow up the sunshine,
Little wind, blow off the rain.

Kate Greenaway

Winter days

Biting air
Winds blow
City streets
Under snow

Noses red
Lips sore
Runny eyes
Hands raw

Chimneys smoke
Cars crawl
Piled snow
On garden wall

Slush in gutters
Ice in lanes
Frosty patterns
On window panes

Morning call
Lift up head
Nipped by winter
Stay in bed.

Gareth Owen

The wind in a frolic

The wind one morning sprang up from sleep,
Saying, 'Now for a frolic! now for a leap!
Now for a madcap galloping chase!
I'll make a commotion in every place!'

So it swept with a bustle right through a great
    town,
Cracking the signs and scattering down
Shutters; and whisking with merciless squalls,
Old women's bonnets and gingerbread stalls.

There never was heard a much lustier shout,
As the apples and oranges trundled about;
And the urchins that stand, with their thievish eyes
For ever on watch, ran off each with a prize.

Then away to the fields it went blustering and
    humming,
And the cattle all wondered what monster was
    coming.
It plucked by the tails the grave matronly cows,
And tossed the colts' manes all over their brows;
Till, offended at such an unusual salute,
They all turned their backs and stood sulky and
    mute.

So on it went, capering and playing its pranks, –
Whistling with reeds on the broad river's banks,
Puffing the birds as they sat on the spray,
Or the traveller grave on the King's highway,
It was not too nice to hustle the bags
Of the beggar, and flutter his dirty rags;
'Twas so bold that it feared not to play its joke
With the doctor's wig or the gentleman's cloak.

Through the forest it roared, and cried gaily,
    'Now,
You sturdy old oaks, I'll make you bow!'
And it made them bow without more ado,
For it cracked their great branches through and
    through.

Then it rushed like a monster on cottage and farm,
Striking their dwellers with sudden alarm;
And they ran out like bees in a mid-summer
    swarm;
There were dames with their kerchiefs tied over
    their caps,
To see if their poultry were free from mishaps;

The turkeys they gobbled, the geese screamed
    aloud,
And the hens crept to roost in a terrified crowd;
There was rearing of ladders, and logs were laid
    on,
Where the thatch from the roof threatened soon to
    be gone.

But the wind had swept on, and had met in a lane
With a schoolboy, who panted and struggled in
    vain;
For it tossed him and twirled him, then passed –
    and he stood
With his hat in a pool, and shoes in the mud!

Then away went the wind in its holiday glee,
And now it was far on the billowy sea;
And the lordly ships felt its staggering blow,
And the little boats darted to and fro.

But, lo! it was night, and it sank to rest
On the sea-bird's rock in the gleaming west,
Laughing to think, in its frolicsome fun,
How little of mischief it really had done.

William Howitt

The tough guy of London

Seen from within a heated room,
On a sunny February afternoon,
London looks like
Any other summer's day.

Step out in only
Your shirt and trousers
And, even with a black belt in karate,
An invisible tough guy
With blimey cold hands and feet,
Punches you
Smack on the nose
Straight back in.

Kojo Gyinaye Kyei

*Skitter, scatter, leap
and squeak*

White sheep

White sheep, white sheep
    On a blue hill,
When the wind stops
    You all stand still,
You all run away
    When the winds blow;
White sheep, white sheep,
    Where do you go?

W. H. Davies

Only my opinion

Is a caterpillar ticklish?
    Well, it's always my belief
That he giggles, as he wiggles
    Across a hairy leaf.

Monica Shannon

Slugs

Slugs, slugs
Crawl through the grass,
Watching all the beetles
As they scurry past.

Slugs, slugs
Crawl so slow,
Leaving tracks of silver
Wherever they go.

Slugs, slugs
Crawl all along the wall,
Popping little horns out,
Make no sound at all.

John Kitching

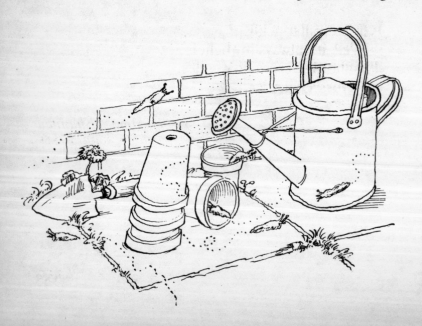

Feather or fur

When you watch for
Feather or fur
Feather or fur
Do not stir
Do not stir.

Feather or fur
Come crawling
Creeping
Some come peeping
Some by night
And some by day.
Most come gently
All come softly
Do not scare
A friend away.

When you watch for
Feather or fur
Feather or fur
Do not stir
Do not stir.

John Becker

A dragonfly

When the heat of the summer
Made drowsy the land,
A dragonfly came
And sat on my hand.

With its blue-jointed body,
And wings like spun glass,
It lit on my fingers
As though they were grass.

Eleanor Farjeon

Hurt no living thing

Hurt no living thing;
Ladybird, nor butterfly,
Nor moth with dusty wing,
Nor cricket chirping cheerily,
Nor grasshopper so light of leap,
Nor dancing gnat, nor beetle fat,
Nor harmless worms that creep.

Christina Rossetti

Shearing day

The sheep are going for shearing,
Listen! Listen!
To the scuffling and the shuffling
And the woolly, muffled ruffling
And the soft pad-pad of feet
On the cobbled village street.

The sheep have been for shearing,
Listen! Listen!
The clipping and the dipping
Is over and they're tripping
New-shorn back down the street,
Cool in the summer's heat.

Daphne Lister

Tigers

I went to the zoo.
The tigers stride
backwards and forwards
safe inside:

Backwards and forwards . . .
Strong and stout
the great bars never
let them out,

But hour on hour
they're bound to go
backwards and forwards,
to and fro . . .

Their eyes are burning
yellow and brown.
They look like the sun
when the sun goes down.

Their muscles ripple
like a sea
under their skin.
They stared at me.

Strange, in a stranger's
land, they are,
with golden fingers
on the fur.

It is a topsy –
turvy thing
that men should catch
and cage a King.

Jean Kenward

Mare

When the mare shows you
her yellow teeth, stuck
with clover and gnawed leaf,
you know they have combed
pastures of spiky grasses,
and tough thickets.

But when you offer her
a sweet, white lump
from the trembling plate
of your palm – she trots
to the gate, sniffs –
and takes it with velvet lips.

Judith Thurman

Poor old horse

My clothing was once of the best woollen twine,
My tail it grew at length, my coat did likewise
   shine:
But now I'm growing old; my beauty does decay.
My master frowns upon me; one day I heard him
   say,
               Poor old horse: poor old horse.

Once I was kept in the stable snug and warm,
To keep my tender limbs from any cold or harm;
But now, in open fields, I am forced for to go,
In all sorts of weather, let it be hail, rain, freeze or
   snow.
               Poor old horse: poor old horse.

Once I was fed on the very best corn and hay
That ever grew in the fields, or in the meadows
   gay;
But now there's no such doing can I find at all,
I'm glad to pick the green sprouts that grow behind
   the wall.
               Poor old horse: poor old horse.

'You are old, you are cold, you are deaf, dull, dumb
   and slow,
You are not fit for anything, or in my team to draw.
You have eaten all my hay, you have spoiled all my
   straw.

So hang him, whip, stick him, to the huntsman let
    him go.'
                    Poor old horse: poor old horse.

My hide unto the tanners then I would freely give,
My body to the hound dogs, I would rather die
    than live,
Likewise my poor old bones that have carried you
    many a mile,
Over hedges, ditches, brooks, bridges, likewise
    gates and stiles.
                    Poor old horse: poor old horse.

Anon

Seal

See how he dives
From rocks with a zoom!
See how he darts
Through his watery room
Past crabs and eels
And green seaweed,
Past fluffs of sandy
Minnow feed!
See how he swims
With a swerve and a twist,
A flip of the flipper,
A flick of the wrist!

Quicksilver-quick,
Softer than spray,
Down he plunges
And sweeps away;
Before you can think,
Before you can utter
Words like 'Dill pickle'
Or 'Apple butter',
Back up he swims
Past sting-ray and shark,
Out with a zoom,
A whoop, a bark;
Before you can say
Whatever you wish,
He plops at your side
With a mouthful of fish!

William Jay Smith

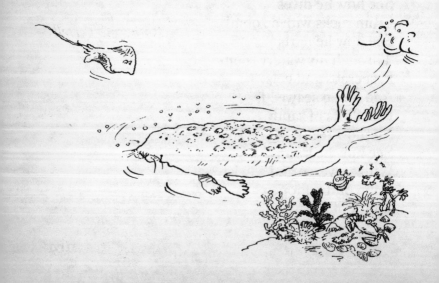

Crabs

Crabs, hiders in rock pools,
Scuttling out sideways when nobody's looking,
Ready to pinch an unwary toe.
How do you manage to disappear so completely
Down into the sand with such incredible speed?
If I manage to catch you
Your small beady eyes seem to look up to heaven,
Imploring to be saved from the fishmonger's slab.
All right, do not worry.
I shall let you go,
If only to see your amazing sideways exit.

Katherine Tyrrell

Black dot

a black dot
a jelly tot

a water-wriggler
a tail jiggler

a leg-kicker
a sitting slicker

a panting puffer
a fly-snuffer

a high-hopper
a belly-flopper

a catalogue
   to make me

     FROG

Libby Houston

Snail

Little snail,
Dreaming you go.
Weather and rose
Is all you know.

Weather and rose
Is all you see,
Drinking
The dewdrop's
Mystery.

Langston Hughes

A bumble-bee

What do I see?
A bumble-bee
Sit on a rose
And wink at me!

What do you mean
By 'Hum, hum, hum'?
If you mean me,
I dare not come!

Anon

Who is so pretty?

Skitter, scatter,
Leap and squeak!
We've been dancing
Half the week.

Under the sofa,
Along the shelf,
Every mouse
Is wild as an elf.

Big round ear
And bright black eye
Nimble and natty,
Limber and spry –

Who is so pretty,
Who is so neat,
As a little mouse dancing
On little grey feet?

Elizabeth Coatsworth

Curiosity

A hedgehog came into our garden today,
Grunting and snuffling and shuffling his way
To where our mother was hanging the washing to
   dry,
In the cold, grey, late November.
Hardly more than a baby, his spikes scarcely stiff;
Two black button eyes; wet, curious snout.
He didn't curl up; he didn't run away –
Perhaps HIS mother wasn't too far away – and felt
Safe enough to let my sister and me
Touch his bristly coat carefully,
Just in case.
We laughed, and we shouted, 'Look Mummy!
        Look Mummy!'
But, before she could turn, he gave
A twitch of his nose, and trotted back
To his mother in the bushes.

Adrian Rumble

Hopping frog

Hopping frog, hop here and be seen,
   I'll not pelt you with stick or stone:
Your cap is laced and your coat is green;
   Goodbye, we'll let each other alone.

Christina Rossetti

I knew a man who always wore a saucepan on his head

Two in bed

When my brother Tommy
Sleeps in bed with me,
He doubles up
And makes
himself
exactly
like
a
V

And 'cause the bed is not so wide,
A part of him is on my side.

A. B. Ross

Mary Ann

He's bought a bed and a table too,
A big tin dish for making stew,
A large flat-iron to iron his shirt,
And a flannel and scrubbing brush to wash away
   the dirt,
And he's bought a pail and basins three,
A coffee pot, kettle, and a teapot for tea,
     And a soup bowl and a ladle,
     And a gridiron and a cradle,
And he's going to marry Mary Ann, that's me!
     He's going to marry Mary Ann!

Joseph Tabrar

A rhyme for a nosey-parker

Ask no questions
And you'll be told no lies;
Shut your mouth
And you'll catch no flies.

Anon

Poem

I loved my friend
He went away from me
There's nothing more to say.
The poem ends,
Soft as it began –
I loved my friend.

Langston Hughes

Mister Beers

This is Mister Beers;
   And for forty-seven years
He's been digging in his garden like a miner.
   He isn't planting seeds
   Nor scratching up the weeds,
He's trying to bore a tunnel down to China.

Hugh Lofting

Jack Hall

Jack Hall,
He is so small,
A mouse could eat him,
Hat and all.

Anon

The folk who live in
Backward Town

The folk who live in Backward Town
Are inside out and upside down.
They wear their hats inside their heads
And go to sleep beneath their beds.
They only eat the apple peeling
And take their walks across the ceiling.

Mary Ann Hoberman

An accident happened to my brother Jim

An accident happened to my brother Jim
When somebody threw a tomato at him –
Tomatoes are juicy and don't hurt the skin,
But this one was specially packed in a tin.

Anon

Allie

Allie, call the birds in,
   The birds from the sky!
Allie calls, Allie sings,
   Down they all fly;
First there came
Two white doves,
   Then a sparrow from her nest,
Then a clucking bantam hen,
   Then a robin red-breast.

Allie, call the beasts in,
   The beasts, every one!
Allie calls, Allie sings,
   In they all run:
First there came
Two black lambs,
   Then a grunting Berkshire sow,
Then a dog without a tail,
   Then a red and white cow.

Allie, call the fish up,
   The fish from the stream!
Allie calls, Allie sings,
   Up they all swim:
First there came
Two gold fish,
   A minnow and a miller's thumb,
Then a school of little trout,
   Then the twisting eels come.

Allie, call the children,
    Call them from the green!
Allie calls, Allie sings,
    Soon they run in:
First there came
Tom and Madge,
    Kate and I who'll not forget
How we played by the water's edge
    Till the April sun set.

Robert Graves

The foolish man

I knew a man who always wore
A saucepan on his head.
I asked him what he did it for.
'I don't know why,' he said.
'It always makes my ears so sore;
I am a foolish man.
I should have left it off before
And worn a frying pan.'

Christopher Chamberlain

Sweeter than sugar

My little baby, little boy blue,
Is as sweet as sugar and cinnamon too;
Isn't this precious darling of ours
Sweeter than dates and cinnamon flowers?

Anon

Hush little baby

Hush, little baby, don't say a word,
Papa's going to buy you a mockingbird.

If the mockingbird won't sing,
Papa's going to buy you a diamond ring.

If the diamond ring turns to brass,
Papa's going to buy you a looking glass.

If the looking glass gets broke,
Papa's going to buy you a billy goat.

If that billy goat runs away,
Papa's going to buy you another today.

Anon

The new neighbour

Have you had your tonsils out?
    Do you go to school?
Do you know that there are frogs
    Down by the Willow Pool?

Are you good at cricket?
    Have you got a bat?
Do you know the proper way
    To feed a white rat?

Are there any apples
    On your apple tree?
Do you think your mother
    Will ask me in to tea?

Rose Fyleman

Sally go round the sun

Sally go round the sun,
Sally go round the moon,
Sally go round the chimney-pots
On a Saturday afternoon.

Anon

Thin Jake

My old friend Jake
was as thin as a snake
and light as a drop of rain.
One windy day
Jake blew away
and was never seen again.

Michael Dugan

Uncle James

My Uncle James
Was a terrible man.
He cooked his wife
In the frying pan.

'She's far too tender
To bake or boil!'
He cooked her up
In peanut oil.

But sometime later –
A month or more –
There came a knock
On my uncle's door.

A great green devil
Was standing there.
He caught my uncle
By the hair.

'Are you the uncle
That cooked his wife,
And leads such a terribly
Wicked life?'

My uncle yowled
Like an old tom cat,
But the devil took him
For all that.

Oh, take a tip
From my Uncle James!
Don't throw stones
And don't call names.

Just be as good
As ever you can –
And never cook aunts
In a frying pan!

Margaret Mahy

Slap Bang

Slap Bang,
   the dirty man,
Washed his face
   in the frying pan,
And after that,
   he skinned the cat,
And made it into
   a hairy hat.

Anon

What somebody said when he was spanked on the day before his birthday

Some day
I may
Pack my bag and run away.
Some day
I may.
– But not today.

Some night
I might
Slip away in the moonlight.
I might
Some night.
– But not tonight.

Some night.
Some day.
I might.
I may.
– But right now I think I'll stay.

John Ciardi

Dan the watchman

Dan the watchman
Doesn't go to bed.
He sits in a little wooden hut
Instead;
At a little coke-fire,
Half red, half blue,
Listening to the owls
Go 'Whoo! Whoo! Whoo!'
And the Town Hall clock
Strike half-past two.

When the moon sits on top
Of the grey church spire,
He puts more coke
On his red-and-blue fire,
When the old mill pond
Begins to freeze,
He eats his supper
Of bread and cheese.

I'd like to go out
In the middle of the night,
When the little coke fire
Is shining bright,
When the flames turn blue,
And the flames burn red,
And everyone else in the world is in bed.
Then I'd sit in the little wooden hut with Dan
And drink strong tea from his black billy can.

John D. Sheridan

The road sweeper

Under the cherries
where nobody goes
sits the road sweeper
a-blowing his nose;

His bread and his billy-can
by him, he wheezes
just like an old badger
and sneezes and sneezes.

Under the cherries
where nobody goes
I saw his handkerchief,
red as a rose.

Jean Kenward

The King of China's daughter

The King of China's daughter,
   So beautiful to see
With her face like yellow water, left
   Her nutmeg tree.
Her little rope for skipping
   She kissed and gave it me –
Made of painted notes of singing-birds
   Among the fields of tea.
I skipped across the nutmeg grove,
   I skipped across the sea;
But neither sun nor moon, my dear,
   Has yet caught me.

Edith Sitwell

Little baby

Little baby, if I threw
This fair blossom down to you,
Would you catch it as you stand,
Holding up each tiny hand,
Looking out of those grey eyes,
Where such deep, deep wonder lies?

Kate Greenaway

Robert Barnes

'Robert Barnes, fellow fine,
Can you shoe this horse of mine?'

'Yes, good sir, that I can,
As well as any other man.
There's a nail, and there's a prod,
And now, good sir, your horse is shod.'

Anon

'Sooeep'

Black as a chimney is his face,
   And ivory white his teeth,
And in his brass-bound cart he rides,
   The chestnut blooms beneath.

'Sooeep, Sooeep!' he cries, and brightly peers
   This way and that, to see
With his two light-blue shining eyes
   What custom there may be.

And once inside the house, he'll squat,
   And drive his rods on high,
Till swirls his sudden sooty brush
   Against the morning sky.

Then 'mid his bulging bags of soot,
   With half the world asleep,
His small cart wheels him off again,
   Still hoarsely bawling, 'Sooeep!'

Walter de la Mare

The babes in the wood

My dear, do you know
How a long time ago
   Two poor little children
Whose names I don't know
Were stolen away
On a fine summer's day
   And left in a wood,
As I've heard people say.

And when it was night,
So sad was their plight,
   The sun it went down
And the moon gave no light!
They sobbed and they sighed,
And they bitterly cried,
   And the poor little things,
They lay down and died.

The robins so red
Brought strawberry leaves
   And over them spread,
And all the day long
They sang them this song:
Poor babes in the wood!
Poor babes in the wood!
   And don't you remember
The babes in the wood?

Anon

Curlylocks

Curlylocks, Curlylocks,
  Wilt thou be mine?
Thou shalt not wash dishes,
  Nor yet feed the swine;
But sit on a cushion,
  And sew a fine seam,
And feed upon strawberries,
  Sugar and cream.

Anon

See the robbers passing by

See the robbers passing by,
  Passing by, passing by;
See the robbers passing by,
  My fair lady.

'What have the robbers done to you,
  Done to you, done to you;
What have the robbers done to you,
  My fair lady?'

'Broke the lock and stole the key,
  Stole the key, stole the key;
Broke the lock and stole the key!
  My fair lady.'

'How many pounds will set you free,
  Set you free, set you free;
How many pounds will set you free;
  My fair lady?'

'Twenty pounds will set you free,
  Set you free, set you free;
Twenty pounds will set you free,
  My fair lady.'

'So much money I have not got,
  Have not got, have not got;
So much money I have not got!
  My fair lady.'

'Then off to prison you must go,
  You must go, you must go;
Then off to prison you must go,
  My fair lady!'

Anon

Policeman, policeman

Policeman, policeman,
   don't catch me!
Catch that boy
   behind that tree.
He stole apples,
   I stole none;
Put him in the jailhouse,
   just for fun.

Anon

She said I said he lied

She said I said he lied
but I said she said he lied
Then you said she said I said he lied.

He said he didn't lie.

Michael Rosen

Get a move on, Joe,
the stars are in the sky

February twilight

I stood beside a hill
  Smooth with new-laid snow,
A single star looked out
  From the cold evening glow.

There was no other creature
  That saw what I could see –
I stood and watched the evening star
  As long as it watched me.

Sara Teasdale

Greatly shining

Greatly shining,
The Autumn moon floats in the thin sky;
And the fish-ponds shake their backs and flash
  their dragon scales
As she passes over them.

Amy Lowell

Night walk

What are you doing away up there
On your great long legs in the lonely air?
    Come down here, where the scents are sweet,
    Swirling around your great, wide feet.

How can you know of the urgent grass
And the whiff of the wind that will whisper and
  pass
    Or the lure of the dark of the garden hedge
    Or the trail of a cat on the road's black edge?

What are you doing away up there
On your great long legs in the lonely air?
    You miss so much at your great, great height
    When the ground is full of the smells of night.

Hurry then, quickly, and slacken my lead
For the mysteries speak and the messages speed
    With the talking stick and the stone's slow
      mirth
    The four feet find on the secret earth.

Max Fatchen

Twilight

Don't say I didn't tell you
about those creepy noises in the dark wood;
I heard them clearly where alone I stood
for a moment under the staring trees there
disturbing the silent air.

It was only owls.

Don't say I didn't warn you
about those spooky lights on the green pool;
I saw them plainly coming home from school
for a moment just beyond the town
dancing up and down.

It was only stars.

Leonard Clark

Home

Snow in the air tonight,
Roads freeze:
No birds sing, cold trees,
But the kitchen is warm, bright.

Leonard Clark

Stars

Bright stars, light stars,
Shining-in-the-night stars,
Little twinkly, winkly stars,
Deep in the sky!

Yellow stars, red stars,
Shine-when-I'm-in-bed stars,
Oh how many blinky stars,
Far, far away!

Rhoda W. Bacmeister

Shadow dance

O Shadow,
Dear Shadow,
Come, Shadow,
And dance!
On the wall
In the firelight
Let both of
Us prance!
I raise my
Arms, thus!
And you raise
Your arms, so!
And dancing
And leaping
And laughing
We go!
From the wall
To the ceiling,
From ceiling
To wall,
Just you and
I, Shadow,
And none else
At all.

Ivy O. Eastwick

Bedtime

Five minutes, five minutes more, please!
    Let me stay five minutes more!
Can't I just finish the castle
    I'm building here on the floor?
Can't I just finish the story
    I'm reading here in my book?
Can't I just finish this bead-chain –
    It *almost* is finished, look!
Can't I just finish this game, please?
    When a game's once begun
It's a pity never to find out
    Whether you've lost or won.
Can't I just stay five minutes?
    Well, can't I stay just four?
Three minutes, then? two minutes?
    Can't I stay one minute more?

Eleanor Farjeon

Time to go home

Time to go home!
  Says the great steeple clock.
Time to go home!
  Says the gold weathercock.
Down sinks the sun
  In the valleys to sleep;
Lost are the orchards
  In blue shadows deep.
Soft falls the dew
  On cornfield and grass;
Through the dark trees
  The evening airs pass:
Time to go home,
  They murmur and say;
Birds to their homes
  Have all flown away.
Nothing shines now
  But the gold weathercock.
Time to go home!
  Says the great steeple clock.

James Reeves

What did I dream?

What did I dream? I do not know –
   The fragments fly like chaff.
Yet, strange, my mind was tickled so
   I cannot help but laugh.

Pull the curtains close again,
   Tuck me grandly in;
Must a world of humour wane
   Because birds begin

Complaining in a fretful tone,
   Rousing me from sleep –
The finest entertainment known,
   And given rag-cheap?

Robert Graves

Night

My kitten walks on velvet feet
And makes no sound at all;
And in the doorway nightly sits
To watch the darkness fall.

I think he loves the lady, Night,
And feels akin to her
Whose footsteps are as still as his,
Whose touch as soft as fur.

Lois Weakley McKay

My dream

I dreamed a dream next Tuesday week,
    Beneath the apple-trees;
I thought my eyes were big pork-pies,
    And my nose was Stilton cheese.
The clock struck twenty minutes to six,
    When a frog sat on my knee;
I asked him to lend me eighteen pence,
    But he borrowed a shilling off me.

Anon

Hurry home

You had better hurry home for your supper's
    nearly ready,
Your mother's in the kitchen and she's awfully
    wild,
She's been shouting at the cat, and she keeps on
    saying,
'Oh where has he got to, the wretched child?'

She has been to the front door and looked through
    the window
And now she's banging on the frying pan,
The plates and the dishes are all on the table,
So run, my boy, as fast as you can.

Don't you know she's cooking your favourite
    supper,
Potatoes in their jackets and beefsteak pie?
She's made a jug of custard for the pudding in the
    oven,
Get a move on, Joe, the stars are in the sky.

They've all left the factory, the streets will soon be
    empty,
No more playing now, it's time you fed,
It really is a shame to keep your mother waiting,
So come have your supper, and then off to bed.

Leonard Clark

It's dark outside

It's dark outside.
It's dark inside.
It's dark behind the door.

I wonder
if I'm brave enough
to walk across the floor.

I am –
at least I think I am.
I'll try it once and see

if Mum comes up
or stays downstairs
with Dad and cups of tea.

Nancy Chambers

Flashlight

My flashlight tugs me
through the dark
like a hound
with a yellow eye,

sniffs
at the edges
of steep places,

paws
at moles'
and rabbits'
holes,

points its nose
where sharp things
lie asleep –

and then it bounds
ahead of me
on home ground.

Judith Thurman

Is the moon tired?

Is the moon tired? She looks so pale
   Within her misty veil;
She scales the sky from east to west,
   And takes no rest.

Before the coming of the night
   The moon shows papery white;
Before the dawning of the day
   She fades away.

Christina Rossetti

Index of first lines

Index of poets

Acknowledgements

For permission to reprint copyright material the Editor is indebted to:

David Andrews: The Piccalilli Monster. Reprinted by permission of the author.

Rhoda W Bacmeister: Stars from *Stories to Begin On* by Rhoda W Bacmeister. © 1940 E P Dutton renewed 1968 Rhoda W Bacmeister. Reprinted by permission of E P Dutton, a division of the New American Library.

Harry Behn: Adventure and Trees from *The Little Hill: Poems and Pictures* by Harry Behn. Copyright © 1949 renewed 1977 by Alice L Behn. Reprinted by permission of Marion Reiner.

Keith Bosley: Bird Sips Water and Cat Purring from *And I Dance* by Keith Bosley. Reprinted by permission of Angus & Robertson (UK) Ltd.

Lillian Boucher: The Twitchetty Witch. Reprinted by permission of the author.

Nancy Chambers: It's Dark Outside and There's a Red Brick Wall from *Stickleback, Stickleback* by Nancy Chambers (Kestrel Books 1977). Copyright © Nancy Chambers 1977.

Marchette Chute: Drinking Fountain from *Round and About* by Marchette Chute. Copyright © 1957 E P Dutton renewed 1985. Reprinted by permission of the author.

John Ciardi: What Somebody Said When He was Spanked on the Day before His Birthday from *You Know Who* by John Ciardi. © John Ciardi 1964. Reprinted by permission of the author.

Leonard Clark: House; Hurry Home; Home from *Collected Poems and Verses* by Leonard Clark. Reprinted by permission of Dobson Books Ltd. Twilight from *Stranger than Unicorns* by Leonard Clark. Reprinted by permission of Dobson Books Ltd.

Elizabeth Coatsworth: November from *Twelve Months Make a Year* by Elizabeth Coatsworth © 1943 Macmillan Publishing Co., renewed 1971 by Elizabeth Coatsworth Beston. Reprinted by permission of Macmillan Publishing Co. Sea gull from *Summer Green* by Elizabeth Coatsworth © 1947 by Macmillan Publishing Co. renewed 1975 by Elizabeth Coatsworth Beston. Reprinted by permission of Macmillan Publishing Co. Who is so pretty? From *Mouse Chorus* by Elizabeth Coatsworth © 1955 Pantheon Books Inc. Reprinted by permission of Pantheon Books, a division of Random House Inc.

	Smith. Reprinted by permission of Burke Publishing Co. Ltd.
William Jay Smith:	Seal from *Laughing Time: Nonsense Poems* by William Jay Smith published by Seymour Lawrence/Delacorte Press 1980. © 1955, 1980 William Jay Smith. Reprinted by permission of William Jay Smith.
Sara Teasdale:	February Twilight and April from *Collected Poems* by Sara Teasdale © 1926 Macmillan Publishing Co. renewed 1954 Mamie T Wheless. Reprinted by permission of Macmillan Publishing Co. © 1915 renewed 1943 Mamie T Wheless.
J. R. R. Tolkien:	Roads Go Ever On from *The Hobbit*. Reprinted by permission of George Allen & Unwin Ltd.
William Carlos Williams:	This is Just to Say from *The Collected Earlier Poems*. Proprietors New Directions Corp. Reprinted by permission of Laurence Pollinger Ltd.
Valerie Worth	Raw carrots from *Small Poems* by Valerie Worth. © 1972 by Valerie Worth. Reprinted by permission of Farrar, Straus & Giroux, Inc.
Peter Young:	Hands from *Passwords* Book 1 by Rose and Young. © Oliver & Boyd Ltd. Published by Longman. Reprinted by permission of Peter Young.
Charlotte Zolotow:	Little Bird from *River Winding*. Reprinted by permission of Abelard & Schuman Publishers.

Every effort has been made to trace the owners of copyright, but we take this opportunity of tendering apologies to any owners whose rights have been unwittingly infringed.

A BOOK OF MILLIGANIMALS
SILLY VERSE FOR KIDS
Spike Milligan

Two more collections of lunatic verse, which work like a dream.

PLEASE MRS BUTLER
Allan Ahlberg

A witty collection of poems about school that will instantly strike a chord of recognition in pupils and teachers alike. Lively illustrations by Fritz Wegner.

FIGGIE HOBBIN
Charles Causley

One of the most popular books of poems for children to have been produced in the last decade, the wide-ranging contents have a strong Cornish flavour.

HOT DOG AND OTHER POEMS
Kit Wright

Kit Wright is superbly witty about the things we all love to hate and has a tremendous time with people who get their comeuppance.

WOULDN'T YOU LIKE TO KNOW
Michael Rosen

A collections of forty poems, including some specially written for Puffin, from a regular contributor to the children's poetry column in the *Sunday Times* colour magazine.

POEMS FOR OVER 10-YEAR-OLDS
ed. Kit Wright

A marvellously varied anthology that will delight, excite, frighten, amuse and inspire all readers of ten and over.

POEMS FOR 9-YEAR-OLDS AND UNDER
ed. Kit Wright

A lighthearted collection, from writers old, modern and anonymous: some full of laughter, nonsense and sheer fun, and some to think about too.

POEMS FOR 7-YEAR-OLDS AND UNDER
ed. Helen Nicholl

A rich and inviting collection of verse, riddles, and limericks, specially chosen for children of seven and under.

THE WANDERING MOON AND OTHER POEMS
James Reeves

A masterly collection of poems for children, with illustrations by Edward Ardizzone.

NINE O'CLOCK BELL
ed. Raymond Wilson

A collection of poems about school.

OF CATERPILLARS, CATS AND CATTLE
Chosen by Anne Harvey

Dogs and frogs, cats and bats, dragonflies and butterflies . . . all these creatures and more are to be found in the poems that make up this delightful anthology selected by Anne Harvey.

Poems short and long, funny and sad, classic and modern; a very varied and enjoyable collection that will appeal to a wide range of readers.

SELECTED CAUTIONARY VERSES
Hilaire Belloc

Funny and famous cautionary tales in verse.

THE PUFFIN BOOK OF MAGIC VERSE
ed. Charles Causley

Every kind of magic is reflected in the poems in this splendid anthology.

DUCKS AND DRAGONS
ed. Gene Kemp

Children take to poetry like ducks to water, says Gene Kemp in the introduction to her anthology. A wide variety of poems, all tried and tested in the classroom.

YOU TELL ME
Roger McGough and Michael Rosen

A collection of largely humorous poems by two well-known poets. Sad, funny, serious and zany, they reflect thoughtfully on everyday life.

CUSTARD AND COMPANY
Ogden Nash

A selection of Ogden Nash's humorous verse for children, selected and illustrated profusely by Quentin Blake.

I LIKE THIS POEM
ed. Kaye Webb

A unique collection of poems chosen by children for children. Illustrated by Antony Maitland.

THE EARTHSICK ASTRONAUT

In this original and exciting collection of children's poems, chosen from entries to the *Observer* National Children's Poetry Competition, the earth is seen through many different eyes. Viewed from a distance by the astronaut and from the closest of quarters by the worm and the mole, our planet and its inhabitants show an infinite variety of shape and character, all drawn in vivid images by some of today's most promising young poets.